Praise from readers

Dr. David Schechter was influential in helping to guide me through my own recovery from chronic pain and introduced me to the world of TMS. *Lessons* is an important work that captures Dr. Sarno's massive contribution to the field of mind-body medicine.

Alan Gordon, LCSW, Psychotherapist
Author of *The Way Out*

Dr. Schechter gives us a rare and fascinating glimpse into Dr. Sarno's life. I learned a lot about mentorship and the legacy of the pioneer of TMS.

Justin Barker, PsyD, Clinical Psychologist West LA
co-author, The MindBody Workbook, Volume Two

Lessons tells the story of how an open-minded medical student with a sore knee took to the "great truth" about chronic pain taught to him by Dr. John Sarno. Dr. Schechter then devoted a good portion of his career to treating patients and teaching others in an environment that was not always favorable. I loved learning what Dr. Sarno often did before his famous TMS lectures… you might not guess!"

Albert Navarra, Esq.
Attorney, Author of The Joy of Argument

I liked *Lessons* which has a good balance of recognizing/celebrating Dr. Sarno and his work, and more personal stories about Dr. Schechter's experiences and TMS journey. I like how he doesn't shy away from talking about the rockier parts of his long relationship with Dr. Sarno which highlights how value can still be found even in disagreement!

Christabelle Junaidi, BS
Medical Assistant, Medical Student 2024

Dr. Schechter and I have collaborated on patient care for over ten years. It was such a pleasure to read this short memoir of what he learned through his long and interesting association with Dr. Sarno.

Hasanna Fletcher, MFT
Therapist, Santa Cruz

In *The Lessons Doctor Sarno Taught Me* – a wonderful and enriching memoir by Dr. David Schechter, one of Dr. Sarno's first mentees – we are treated to rare glimpses of Sarno as he pens the first of his four books, *Mind Over Back Pain,* and works to disseminate his mind/body understandings and treatments for patients with chronic pain. Millions of people, caregivers and sufferers, who have benefitted from Sarno's teachings will no doubt delight in these intimate and humanizing vignettes.

Steve Bierman, M.D.
Author of *Healing*

THE LESSONS DOCTOR SARNO TAUGHT ME

REFLECTIONS, MEMOIR, AND TEACHINGS

David Schechter, M.D.

Dedication

To the memory of John E. Sarno, M.D.

a physician who cured so many,
observed so well,
and stuck to his beliefs

MINDBODY MEDICINE PUBLICATIONS

Contents

Introduction

Many people know about Dr. Sarno's unique and powerful approach to treating pain and other disorders for which stress and emotions play a role. He wrote books about the condition he called TMS and I and other authors have written books that build upon his essential teachings. His books continue to be popular, despite his passing, and will likely be so for decades to come because of his important message and the manner in which he was able to convey ideas that allows the reader to see him/herself in each chapter.

There are no biographies of Dr. Sarno currently and he did not write an autobiography. I believe that people want to learn more about him, as well. He was a confident and important man. He was an independent thinker and a keen observer of his patients. He was an innovator.

My goal here is to share the lessons that Dr. Sarno taught me and I learned from him. I will share some of the experiences I had with him and how this has impacted my practice, my patients, and my life over the last four decades.

I trust that you will find these teachings valuable and that by sharing my experiences with Dr. Sarno the reader will gain additional insight into their own personal and professional growth and well-being.

This is not a biography. Consider it an extended essay conveying the teachings of Dr. John Sarno, as interpreted by me and my experiences with him. It has an element of memoir from my perspective, as well. The book is designed for the lay public interested in Dr. Sarno and for professionals. Both those familiar with his work and those who are not should find something of value here.

Dr. Sarno's 100th Birthday would have been on June 23, 2023.

Preface

Dr. Sarno was brilliant and a powerful force of nature. As I elaborated in *Think Away Your Pain*, I believe his work should have received a Nobel Prize in Medicine. His contributions to mind-body medicine and to pain medicine are transformational. His work, however, is still poorly understood and even misunderstood by many of those physicians who are even aware of his work.

Despite this, he treated and healed so many people! Directly in his office and hospital, tens of thousands. From his books, hundreds of thousands more. From his influence on the next generation of TMS physicians, psychologists, and psychotherapists many tens or hundreds of thousands more. All together, his books, other author's books on TMS, and patient care– millions of people have been positively affected.

I hope that he will receive further recognition for his work in the future. In the meantime, he serves as continued inspiration in the present, for patients, doctors, and therapists—the entire community of people focused on healing utilizing the principles he described.

These approaches continue to evolve which is both natural and desirable. Knowledge continues to grow in brain science, the central nervous system, nerve pathways and the like. Psychology also continues to evolve and in the TMS field has been shaped by his contributions but also by other psychological theories, principles, and approaches.

This short book is arranged in a somewhat chronological fashion, from our first meeting in 1981 to the present. I learned many lessons from Dr. Sarno and from my interaction with him over the decades that followed that initial meeting. His was the single biggest contribution to my professional career as a physician.

To acknowledge his massive contributions to the field of pain treatment and mind-body medicine is not to imply his perfection or his omniscience. For this reason, I share experiences and perspectives I have that some devotees may feel diminish his reputation. My intention is to be truthful. No man is perfect. Lincoln wasn't perfect. Martin Luther King, Jr. wasn't perfect.

In the next twelve chapters, with eighteen lessons, I will share what I learned from Dr. Sarno.

CHAPTER 1

Our Early Interactions

MEDICAL STUDENTS STUDY ANATOMY IN the first year of medical school. Typically, the course starts during the first semester, even the first week of school. It is one of the touchpoints of medical education with the dissection of a cadaver and the intimate study of the internal organs and structures of the human body.

My favorite section of anatomy was the musculoskeletal and this likely explains how I gravitated towards Sports Medicine in my career and musculoskeletal medicine. Most of the instructors were anatomy professors in the medical school. They were not practicing physicians, but usually Ph.D. 's in an anatomy related field.

Occasionally a guest lecturer was invited, and this is how I first learned of Dr. John Sarno. He spoke to our class about the practical anatomy of the musculoskeletal system. As the Director of Outpatient Rehabilitation Medicine at the Rusk Institute of

Rehabilitation Medicine, he was an expert in this area. I enjoyed his talk. It was very clear and well-organized. In this lecture, he did not speak at all about mind-body or psycho-physiologic concepts.

I also learned a bit more about the Rusk Institute of Rehabilitation Medicine when the aging Dr. Howard Rusk, the 'father of Rehabilitation Medicine' spoke to our first year class. I recall he handed out a pre-signed copy of his book to each of us after the class. Dr. Rusk pioneered the field of Rehabilitation Medicine during World War II when he realized that soldiers who healed from a wound or injury got reinjured if sent back to the fight without first getting their bodies stronger.

Much later, he encouraged Dr. Sarno to pursue Rehabilitation Medicine when Dr. Sarno decided to transition from being a small-town Family Medicine Doctor to develop an academic career. Thus, Dr. Rusk played a role in bringing Dr. Sarno to the NYU Medical Center and he encouraged his career in this academic environment. Dr. Sarno's earlier work on Stroke symptoms and rehabilitation led to many publications in the medical literature. These two lectures eventually sparked my interest in meeting with Dr. Sarno about a knee issue from which I was suffering.

NYU (New York University) Medical School is situated on First Avenue and along the East River in

Manhattan and at that time there was a basketball court behind the student dorms. The court was a long stone's throw from the East River Drive highway, also called the FDR Drive. That small outdoor space was an important area for me. It was a place to get outside, socialize with fellow students, and compete in basketball, my sport of choice at that time. I also liked to run and there was a fun urban run along the East River that took you down to the Williamsburg and Brooklyn Bridges if you felt like a long run. The views were amazing along that running path, as well.

Anyway, my knee began to hurt and gradually kept getting worse. I made an appointment with the Medical School Student Health physician and was examined and prescribed some anti-inflammatory medication. I had no real improvement and much frustration as I had curtailed basketball and running, the two active forms of stress release I was relying on to get me through the challenges and pressures of that first year of medical school.

I went back to the student health doctor unimproved and he advised me to see an Orthopedist. As a student, he was able to get me an appointment with a renowned Orthopedist, coincidentally the New York Yankees team physician, at the time. He examined me and advised strengthening exercises with leg weights after finding not that much during an exam. I did them diligently and noticed a lot more strength in my quads, but no less pain in my knee!

At some point I saw a podiatrist who diagnosed flat feet, which I knew I had and he made some orthotics (arch supports) for me. The results– a better foot position when walking, perhaps, but the pain persisted.

I returned to the Orthopedist, and he told me I should get a knee arthrogram. My bad luck here was that the MRI was invented and available for clinical use the very next year. MRI scans are non-invasive. The arthrogram, however, involved inserting a long needle into the knee and injecting a whole lot of dye. Since this was a teaching hospital, a radiology resident did the injecting, and not so smoothly. Images were reviewed, and I was told I had no clear tear or other significant finding on the menisci, the cushioning cartilage that they thought might be torn.

So, it was back to the knee exercises and no one had really diagnosed the problem or come close to solving it. As a conscientious medical student and class A worrier, I hit the books, in the medical school library, to find an answer. What I found, about knees, about flat feet, about tibial torsion (bow leggedness) did not lead me to pain relief but did lead me to more worry and fear that I wouldn't get better and be able to return to sports. I experienced the dreaded vicious cycle of worry and pain that is so common.

So, I decided I would seek out another approach, another opinion. I looked up Dr. Sarno's office and I walked over to the Rusk Institute and into his office. I asked his secretary if I might ask him a question and fortunately, he had a few minutes to talk. I walked in and saw him, neatly dressed, hair combed precisely, standing erect. I introduced myself and I told him, concisely, the story. A capsule version. My internal goal was high-tech physical therapy, I thought.

His response: "I don't know what you'll make of this, son, but 95% of chronic pain is psychosomatic". He waited for a response, as I was still recovering from the shock/surprise that I felt from his statement. I mumbled something about migraine headaches and stress, and he interrupted to say that he understood if I was a bit skeptical. He invited me to come to the seminar/lecture he gave to his patients the following Monday and if I were interested after that, he would see me as a patient, on a courtesy basis.

He was direct with me, no nonsense, but with an overarching theme of trying to help.

I thanked him for his time and walked back to the school to think this over. I decided I would definitely attend the seminar.

LESSON ONE

95% of chronic pain is psychosomatic.

Do I believe this? It is impossible to say for sure, but here is what I have taken from this comment all these years later. First, a lot of chronic pain is a mind-body disorder, we'll call it TMS (tension myoneural syndrome) and explain the term later (or see References). Second, if you have TMS as the explanation for your pain, and you are open to this diagnosis, you have a great opportunity to get better or completely cure the problem. Third, other approaches to chronic pain have a low success rate, are invasive, often expensive, and can be toxic or addictive.

So, I attended the lecture/discussion the following Monday, about 6 PM, in a medium-sized conference room in the Rusk Institute in 1981. Perhaps 30 people are in attendance– patients and some spouses and friends. Dr. Sarno stands at the front, wearing a bow tie, calm and confident appearing, and begins his presentation. He uses a slide projector and speaks confidently, forcefully, and enunciates clearly. He is short of stature, but strong of voice. The concepts are presented along with a small amount of data he had, at that point, on his patients and their associated conditions. What he said made a ton of sense to me, a first-year medical student sitting toward the front, in my corduroy pants and plaid button-down shirt. The remainder of the audience were well dressed New Yorkers in their 30s, 40s, and 50s, who also seemed to be fascinated by the talk.

In addition to the logical content, he presented with a confident forcefulness that was reassuring. This was characteristic of his interactions with patients as well.

LESSON TWO

It can be effective to get patients together in a room and talk to them, to teach them.

Years later, I began doing my own evening seminars in Los Angeles to an excellent reception. Challenges in L.A. include the widely spread-out city, horrible traffic, and work/family conflicts. Eventually I transitioned to other teaching methods that focused on a home based educational program, including audiocassettes, later CD's, VHS tapes, later DVD's, Workbooks, online programs, and the like. Now we have Zoom and I have been doing a weekly online group for the last few years, co-led by a psychologist, in this virtual but highly effective format. I also have an online course with video; unthinkable in that pre-internet era.

I spoke with Dr. Sarno briefly after the lecture, thanking him for the invitation to attend his presentation and I went home to ponder what he had said. As I have detailed elsewhere, once reaching my apartment and sitting on my bed, a feeling that a weight was lifting off my shoulders was palpable. This weight, this albatross, was the fear of not finding a diagnosis, not finding a solution to my pain. That evening I felt strongly that I had found that solution and the days and weeks that followed reinforced this belief as my pain began to dramatically diminish. Over the following weeks I started shooting free throws, doing some jogging, and eventually returned to basketball without pain! I even captained an intramural team called "Schechter's Dissectors". The name was created by some teammates!

Along the way, I made an appointment to see him and he did a consultation on me including a physical exam (I did have the tender points) and Dr. Sarno confirmed the diagnosis of TMS.

LESSON THREE

If you are a little desperate and you are open to this diagnosis, it can be transformative.

Years later, Dr. Sarno told me he thought that only 15% of potential patients with pain would accept a psychophysiologic diagnosis. We discussed why that might be and I acknowledged that there are many patients who are not open to TMS. Over the years I have thought about this issue a lot and worked on a lot of different ways to present these concepts so that they can be more readily accepted, understood, and believed. Society has also changed a bit and I do believe more people are open to the mind-body linkage than they were all those years ago.

LESSON FOUR

Not everyone is going to accept the diagnosis of TMS. That is going to be one of the challenges in making this type of treatment more readily available.

We need to, in a way, prepare society for this type of diagnosis and approach. I have been developing a program for high school students that can be taught by their health education teacher, to introduce them to mind-body concepts. Perhaps this awareness may even inoculate them, to some degree, against these psycho-physiologic disorders. The books, movies, online videos, podcasts and other media on this subject have certainly broadened its exposure to the world. I even gave a talk in Israel earlier this year to an interested group of professionals.

CHAPTER 2

Research Study

Ponder this. I was a medical student; I've just had a transformative experience in relation to my own health. I want to share this with my friends, my classmates, and my professors. What is the reaction? Skepticism, denial, scoffing and lack of interest! I am very disappointed.

My own background included an interest in the history and sociology of medicine. I took a course in Medical Sociology as a college student at Princeton. One of the readings was a seminal article by George Engel, M.D. (see references) from the University of Rochester. Dr. Engel called this model of medicine– biopsychosocial. No one had put these word bits together before. He did so to convey the importance of looking at patients, of looking at health, and disease in a comprehensive way.

Reductionism, the breaking down of scientific and medical facts to their smallest components, has helped medicine progress through the antibiotic era and beyond. But Engel wrote convincingly that humans are complicated and that an approach that considers one's biology (BIO), one's psychology (PSYCHO) and one's social environment (SOCIAL) was a key to better health care. I instinctively agreed. It made total sense to me. This model was especially important for chronic issues.

But apparently it did not grab many medical students or doctors at NYU. Doctors are selected for their science aptitude, their ability to take tests, their energy and passion about medicine, but not really for their psychological insightfulness. At least that has been my experience. There are many exceptions of course. But few, if any, were at NYU at that time.

LESSON FIVE

Doctors are difficult to convince about the reality and effectiveness of TMS.

This lesson has proven to be a challenge to this very day. I later learned from Dr. Sarno, that despite practicing in the Rusk Institute (later Institute of Rehabilitation Medicine, or IRM), he had perhaps one or two referrals per year from all the NYU physicians. There is a First Avenue Corridor between 24th Street and 34th Street where the medical school and its affiliated hospitals are located. 600-700 physicians, perhaps more, and so few referrals. This despite the fact that some of their patients must have spoken of Dr. Sarno's success with chronic pain, and with back pain. Very disappointing and discouraging.

Back to my pain issue. I did receive a consultation with Dr. Sarno. He had an interesting style of practice, which I got to see daily during the summer I spent in his office. But for my consultation, we talked in his small office/consultation room for twenty minutes about my history and issues. We walked into an even smaller examination room where he checked my reflexes and pressed for the 'tender points' characteristic of TMS. I got dressed and walked back to the consultation room to finish up. Dr. Sarno changed the table paper himself. This was a necessity but also a reminder that one can do great work with a small office and changing table paper oneself.

LESSON SIX

There is nothing wrong with tidying up the office yourself. Even a Professor of Rehabilitation Medicine chose to do it himself.

LESSON SIX (A)

The size of one's office does not determine the importance of what a doctor has to say to you.

At one point in my career, I was transitioning into full-time private practice. I had spent nearly a decade where I combined part-time practice and teaching at a residency program. I too had a tiny office at first. But soon, I had a big practice... and eventually a larger space to work.

I kept in touch with Dr. Sarno about my rapid clinical improvement and I attended the full 3-week lecture series he had at that time. Coincidentally, I had already arranged a summer experience for that summer, in Rehabilitation Medicine, so I saw him sporadically during that summer. I asked him if he was interested in having me as a research assistant to do a study, at some point, and he said he was.

The following year, still excited about the TMS cure, I investigated summer grants and fellowships that might allow me to do research with Dr. Sarno. I obtained a work-study grant, and this allowed me to spend my summer in his office suite. I was able to use a vacant office not far from his, in the same suite. My fascinating summer consisted of seeing patients with him, co-creating a research plan, and doing the research data collection. I was able to attend his weekly lectures and we spent some time together on those late Monday afternoons between the work day and the early evening lecture which started at six pm. Dr. Sarno liked to walk to a particular tiny grocery store and get a beer before his lecture. I would walk with him, although I don't recall drinking with him, for some reason.

Dr. Sarno described to me an overview of the research study he wanted me to do but I was given some freedom to fill in the details in terms of how to collect the data, questions to ask, and statistical analysis and the like. He indicated an interest in publishing the paper in a major journal. He told me I could write the methods and results and he would write the introduction, discussion, and the like. It seemed like a wonderful opportunity at many levels.

LESSON SEVEN

If you find the right person to work on a project, giving them some slack can be very productive for all.

Perhaps the most amazing part began with pulling a couple of hundred charts off his chart rack at random and organizing these charts so that I could begin calling patients about their outcomes. When I made those telephone calls, I kept hearing accounts of "medical miracles". People who had failed other treatments got better with Dr. Sarno's diagnosis, lectures, and this treatment method. So, it wasn't just me, it was a lot of folks! I could also see how his treatment method had evolved. Early on, he included physical therapy with the educational and psychological components. Then he decided to eliminate the physical treatments as being counterproductive to the goal.

I spoke with 177 patients and compiled the data then analyzed it. While it was not a placebo-controlled, or double-blinded study, it was a remarkable outcome study of a cohort of people with mostly chronic back pain. The project solidified my interest in TMS. Learning from Dr. Sarno's interactions with dozens of patients and attending multiple lectures that he gave was a fantastic opportunity. I even got to spend some time with his amazing and accomplished wife, Martha Taylor Sarno, and his then little daughter Christina (now a grown woman and a psychotherapist!). His long-time secretary Mary even warmed up a bit by the end of the summer. She was efficient and protective of him.

I was even invited to his summer home which was by a lake in Connecticut, if I recall correctly. During this weekend, I got to see him as a family man, see the pride he had in his energy efficient passive solar home (far ahead of his time in this regard as well), and see him relax a bit sharing walks and hikes with his family including his young daughter. I even saw him without a tie or bow tie in this casual environment. We shared an interest in health conscious eating. Perhaps that helped him live a long life.

At the end of the summer, I wrote up the parts of the research that I understood to be my responsibility for the research paper. I showed them to Dr. Sarno. He thought they were fine but told me that his goal for the research data was to include it in his upcoming book. Later, he suggested, we could complete a paper and submit it. His first priority, he emphasized, was the book.

This was not at all my understanding of the summer project and I had an excellent recollection of the conversation I had with Dr. Sarno about his goals and mine for the summer research project (funded by a work-study grant). He had never mentioned a book project to me until well after I started on the summer project. This book was to be his first on this subject, later entitled, *Mind Over Back Pain*.

At some point he asked me to read his manuscript and I made some suggestions to help with the readability and clarity of the book. After all, I was far closer to being a lay person than he was, a doctor who had already practiced for many years. This gave me some advantage in responding to the manuscript from the perspective of a lay reader, a successful patient myself, and yet someone with the knowledge of TMS that few others had at that time.

He worked on the book for additional months, along with his editors at the publishing company.

While not the best of his four books on TMS, it will always be the first. I was honored by being acknowledged in the book, in a prominent position. He mentioned me, in the Acknowledgments Section, after his wife Martha and before Howard Rusk, M.D., the father of Rehabilitation Medicine!

At some point, we talked more about submitting the data as a research paper. He shared the data in his lecture series and when I attended, he mentioned my participation in the research. My humility was further developed when my name did not appear in the text or notes of the book as having "done the data collection" as his research assistant. My frustration built further when he indicated to me that the research was good but was not up to the standards of major research publications. I disagreed, but I was a medical student, and he was a Professor at NYU.

LESSON EIGHT

You do not always get what you want. Mentors are not perfect.

LESSON EIGHT (A)

When you are in a position of being the boss, give credit to those who assist and make them co-authors on your published papers.

So not all the Lessons in this book are based upon purely positive experiences. It is hard to have a long-term relationship (albeit intermittent and primarily of a professional and later collegial manner) without some disappointments and frustrations. It took a long while for me to get over these feelings, but I learned to accept the good with the bad when it comes to the tremendous amount that I learned from Dr. Sarno early in my career. Also, to the professional boost that knowing and practicing this work has meant to me over the ensuing decades.

I was disappointed at the time. I am far from ungrateful, however. I am extremely grateful for the opportunity to learn from Dr. Sarno and receive referrals from him for about twenty years, until he retired. And to remain as friends in his later years, speaking or writing to one another from time to time. He usually wrote me handwritten notes of thanks and encouragement in response to, for example, a Christmas gift that I would have shipped to his office or home. (see Appendix A)

CHAPTER 3

Taking it Into Training

So, after these amazing experiences as a first- and second-year medical student, it was time to get down to the clinical training by the rest (not the best) of NYU Medical School and affiliated hospitals. I did my required rotations—the intense inpatient psychiatric at old Bellevue Hospital—a locked ward, there are stories to tell of that experience, I assure you.

I rotated through Obstetrics and delivered my first baby (and second and ….). On to Pediatrics and the highs and lows of dealing with sick and well children, in the hospital and in the clinics. Finally Internal Medicine, the core of the NYU experience, and Surgery at the Veteran's Hospital in Manhattan, a professionally empowering experience as well. Then there were electives and Family Medicine rotations in exotic cities like Kingston and Utica, New York. I even did a West Coast trip for a month of clinical rotation at Northridge Hospital in the San Fernando Valley of Los Angeles.

I was busy, learning a lot, but TMS and my biopsychosocial orientation informed my worldview and my practice approach. I tried to get to know my patients. I spent time at their bedsides talking to them and learned a lot about them. My supervising interns and residents were sometimes pleased by what I could add, both medically and psychosocially to patient care. Other times, they were dismayed that I got too close to or spent too much time talking to my patients. Dealing with mostly hospitalized, sicker patients, TMS did not come up as a diagnosis too often but I tried to offer an integrative approach as I worked up my patients and "treated" them as part of the inpatient team.

I thought about going into Dr. Sarno's specialty of Physical Medicine and Rehabilitation (Physiatry or PM and R) but decided on Family Practice (now Family Medicine) instead. Interestingly, that was his first endeavor after his internship and after Columbia Medical School, which he attended. He practiced in upstate New York, I believe, and delivered babies. He did full-service General Practice as they called it at that time.

I felt that Family Medicine was a field that was the most savvy about psychosocial aspects of health and disease for all kinds of patients and that PM and R, from what I saw then, was very biopsychosocial, but mostly for disabled patients. I preferred the broader perspective and opportunity to treat more kinds of patients at that time and applied to Family Medicine residency programs. My top choices included two in Southern California and two in New Jersey. My decisions were driven by my own need to grow and expand my horizons and the quality of the programs of course, along with issues of family, both near and far, and where I might enjoy living as an unmarried resident for three years. When I matched in Santa Monica, living in an apartment nine blocks from the beach seemed quite appealing for those rare days off.

My Residency Program in Family Medicine at Santa Monica Hospital/UCLA was great training in many ways. However, I always felt that the behavioral science education was missing something. It was more behaviorally oriented (in contrast to psychodynamic). Perhaps, in retrospect, I would have preferred Northridge's program which might have been better in that regard. But again, I had experienced the wonders of TMS and this affected my perception of all of this teaching and training. I had experienced TMS as a patient of Dr. Sarno's, a research assistant, a medical student trying to incorporate the work, and even an editorial assistant on his first book. After you've learned advanced calculus, it can be hard to go back and study basic algebra!

LESSON NINE

If TMS really gets into you as a professional in training, it may powerfully shape you for the immediate and longer-term future.

My interactions with Dr. Sarno during these three years were rare. These were the years before email, before texting, before inexpensive or free long-distance calls. I came back to New York twice a year to see my family and I typically tried to see him on one of those occasions, either in his office for a brief chat, or for lunch or dinner. I recall that he and his wife had a favorite restaurant near their home in New York City at which they loved to dine. One of those places where you go often and they learn your name and treat you like a friend.

Sometimes these get-togethers happened, sometimes they did not. He went on with his career, treating TMS patients, and doing more writing (and becoming more well known). I went on with my training and growing up as a young adult doctor. He was gracious to his first TMS disciple, but we drifted apart quite a bit.

As a resident, I continued to try to be biopsychosocial in my perspective on patients. At the same time, I was being professionally socialized for speed, for toughness under pressure, for brief interactions with patients that did not favor this approach. When I saw the TMS diagnosis needed to be made, I also faced the challenge that our clinic population was generally not well educated and communicating the concepts of TMS in a relatively brief interaction was challenging.

The only book out there was the single one by Dr. Sarno. There was no internet yet, no other books, no videos, etc. I had no ability to give lectures to patients in the evening and the psychologists I worked with didn't really get this concept. They had their own way of working with patients.

LESSON TEN

My colleagues who are well meaning, even psychosocially oriented, will be unable to understand or help with TMS treatment unless they learn it and internalize it.

CHAPTER 4

Practice and Reconnecting

After my residency program, I needed to reorient back to life. It was a little (just a little) like a combat soldier coming back to stateside life and needing to decompress and relax. My life was less career focused for a while. I got physician jobs in Urgent Care after residency and had the opportunity to travel, date, and live in a much less intense way than the three years of residency, which were of course preceded by four years of medical school. My first AOL email address was MisterVacation or something of that sort!

I recall working at an Urgent Care center near LAX, the LA Airport. It was called the Airport Medical Center. We saw a lot of injured workers, from flight attendants and pilots to baggage handlers, as well as travelers to and from dozens of countries. I even learned a little medical Japanese that I still remember, but rarely use. One day my colleague was talking to an injured worker about his neck x-rays. The context is that this worker had tweaked his neck lifting a heavy bag and had a soft tissue injury that should resolve in a week or ten days.

But in those days, we still did a lot of x-rays on soft tissue injuries. Many were unnecessary and many would not be done today. My colleague was showing him his neck x-ray and telling him that he had "degenerative" changes in the spine and that was why his neck hurt. I could see the patient's face drop as he heard this disturbing news. I know he would worry about this and it could even affect his recovery from his minor injury. After he left, I spoke to my colleague about how common degenerative changes were and how they were NOT the cause of this man's pain. I think he used that phrase less often thereafter.

LESSON ELEVEN

Once you understand TMS, it really hits you hard when you see doctors misdiagnosing and miscommunicating to patients in ways that are anti-therapeutic.

Eventually all this Urgent Care, Worker's Compensation and the like got tiresome and I got the urge to open a practice. For one thing, I thought I could run one better than or at least as well as the doctors I had worked for. For another, I realized I needed to express myself as a doctor in my own unique ways and not according to someone's else's formulas or approaches. During these years I taught residents and some medical students and that was fun and it gave me a chance to expose them to TMS concepts and principles, a bit. I don't believe any of these trainees really took to the work in a powerful way and none have become known as TMS doctors since then, to my knowledge.

I had an opportunity to ease into starting my own practice in the offices of another doctor who was an Orthopedist. He was intrigued by my Family Medicine/Sports Medicine credentials and thought I would be a good addition to his Center he had created. I had very few patients at first until a fortuitous series of circumstances occurred that led me back to Dr. Sarno, back to TMS work and forward to my ongoing career path.

This actually started with a physical injury. I wore a large backpack on a trip to Europe, the kind that sits low on your hips and straps around your waist. Unfortunately, as a slim individual, with less natural "padding" than most, the straps pressed too forcefully against a particular nerve in my upper thigh and left me, upon my return to the US, with a painful kind of tingling numbness in my right upper thigh. I talked to an older, very respected colleague (PM and

R, actually) who referred me to a younger colleague of his (also PM and R) and I saw him for a consultation in his Beverly Hills office.

While talking I noticed his diplomas, his New York accent and mentioned that I had attended NYU Medical School. Somehow, he or I mentioned Dr. Sarno and the conversation about this continued even after the consultation. This doctor had worked with Dr. Sarno during his residency, and was Dr. Sarno's second disciple, of sorts. Even more interesting was that this colleague had met an entrepreneur and the two of them were working on a program to incorporate TMS approaches into Worker's Compensation Care protocols to lower costs and improve outcomes.

This led to some dinners, some meetings with the businessman and eventually to a request for me to travel to Dr. Sarno, see how interested he was in the Business Proposal and get updated on his work. I spoke with Dr. Sarno on the phone after a pause of a year or two and briefly caught up. I arranged to fly to New York, stay with an old college friend and spend almost a week with Dr. Sarno, talking, seeing patients, catching up and bouncing ideas around.

This turned out better than expected for everything but the business proposition, which ultimately failed to become a business although later we had some amazing meetings at Disney in Orlando and Burbank and with another company. Dr. Sarno saw my excitement and fascination about TMS again, I got to see patients with him, this time as a full-fledged doctor, and we spent some time talking over dinner. I believe I also had an opportunity to spend a little time with his wife, Martha, on this trip as well.

At the end of my week in New York, I said goodbye to Dr. Sarno. He asked me if I was diagnosing and treating TMS in Los Angeles. I told him I was, but I had very few patients open to the diagnosis (an ongoing issue for any practitioner working with potential TMS patients). He asked if I had a practice that he could refer patients to and for a business card. I gladly gave him one, but honestly thought that referrals from thousands of miles away would happen rarely, if at all.

LESSON TWELVE

In the modern age, a well-known practitioner who patients want to see cannot treat everyone in his region much less the country and will need colleagues to refer to.

What had happened since I attended medical school and worked with Dr. Sarno? Well ten years had passed. Dr. Sarno was incredibly popular in New York by word of mouth and word of magazine (he had been written up in a popular magazine some years before). He had written and published his second book *Healing Back Pain*, which became a bestseller, and had gotten a lot more awareness of his work from this, at least from prospective patients. And the internet had started to awaken.

I got back to Los Angeles, to my office space that I sublet part-time from the Orthopedist, and the phone started to ring. It was fun and exciting. I was getting calls from patients that had called Dr. Sarno's office and either he or his secretary had said that I was the doctor to see in Los Angeles—even throughout California, for that matter. I got calls from San Francisco, from San Diego, and occasionally from nearby states.

I trained my staff about TMS and we started making lots of longer appointments for prospective TMS patients. What was different? Not just being busier, but also these individuals were already open to and a little bit informed about the diagnosis because they had read his book (or sometimes heard about it from someone else who had read it). Or they saw a TV interview he had done.

LESSON THIRTEEN

If a patient is receptive to TMS, they can be more easily and more effectively treated.

CHAPTER 5

The Busy State-Wide Practice

I saw a lot of patients and I developed my own evening lecture/seminar modeled on Dr. Sarno's approach. Patients enjoyed this, often bringing with them a spouse or a friend, and the event was educational but also interactive as members of the audience interacted with one another and answered questions. I could see the power of this model and continued it. Dr. Sarno had taught me that education was the "penicillin" for TMS/chronic pain.

LESSON FOURTEEN

Education is akin to a medication for TMS.

Some patients require more than just education, however. For a while I also did a more psychological TMS group, along with a psychotherapist, Donald Dubin, whom I met when we had a mutual patient.

Don, like many of the TMS practitioners nationally, had found one of Dr. Sarno's books himself. He applied it to his own back pain, got relief and began to discuss it with patients. After he and I met, I had another essential element of a great TMS program, a psychotherapist to refer patients to for therapy. Don was the first in LA and there have been many more.

Our attempts at creating and keeping a TMS therapy group (with Don and me leading the group) proved challenging as people in L.A. are very spread out. Traffic is terrible and it's hard to get to a location. No place is the center, like some other cities, and fortunately, people got better and got on with their lives.

It has taken a pandemic and Zoom for me to try TMS group sessions again and under these circumstances, with no physical commute and high convenience, they have proven successful. Dr. Sarno pioneered groups with Arlene Feinblatt, Ph.D. decades before in New York City and was able to use them for patients who struggled a bit to improve. Dr. Feinblatt was the pioneer of TMS psychotherapy, working closely with Dr. Sarno, especially in the early years of his treatment program. She also trained or helped train other prominent TMS therapists including Fran Anderson and Eric Sherman who continue to practice in New York.

CHAPTER 6

The Workbook

Dr. Sarno mentioned writing about feelings in his seminar and in at least one of his books. I began using writing or journaling with my patients early on in my private practice and gradually expanded its use in my work with patients. In 1999, I decided to write a guided journal, *The MindBody Workbook*. This simply designed, spiral bound notebook style book has proven highly effective and popular for over twenty years. My estimate is that between printed and ebook copies, this workbook has been used by over 35,000 people to date.

I have just written *The MindBody Workbook, Volume 2*, along with a colleague in psychology, Justin Barker, Psy.D. This book offers patients an updated program, more psychologically insightful questions and we include affirmations and other innovations. Also, it gives people a second month of guided journaling if they wish to have that structure for a longer period.

People can start with the original or finish with it. The Workbooks fit together in either order. Both Workbooks have been revised to an 8 x 11 printed version, no longer spiral bound.

LESSON FIFTEEN

Expressing feelings is important for TMS and writing is an effective way to do so.

When I showed the original Workbook to Dr. Sarno, he remarked that it was more structured than he was used to working with TMS patients. But he liked it. Eventually I noticed that he began incorporating more specific instructions to patients in his office handouts. I was glad to have contributed to my mentor's practice, in a small way.

Other books were being written about TMS by doctors who had learned from Dr. Sarno or been inspired by his written work. We went from literally being able to count every physician able to treat TMS on the fingers of one hand to a somewhat longer list. Dr. Sarno's list of referrals reminds me of another chapter in our relationship, an element that was not always a positive.

Dr. Sarno is a hugely important figure in Chronic Pain whose work is far more widely known and understood by patients and the lay public than by physicians.

Facing resistance, being ignored at NYU by the many physicians and colleagues who should have been inspired by his work to help patients in pain, was exceedingly difficult. This took a strong personality, a confidence in himself and in his ideas which is quite remarkable.

His confident personality was highly effective for communicating the concepts of TMS to a sometimes-skeptical audience of patients. It was highly effective for sticking to his guns when it came to his ideas and theories about pain. As a mentee, it was occasionally challenging, especially if I suggested alternative explanations for some phenomena or disagreed with something in the TMS arena. This led to occasional clashes and his way of dealing with this was to distance from me for a while.

Dr. Sarno's office kept a list of doctors he referred to in different cities. Eventually, he added a second name in Los Angeles, perhaps a third. At times he became upset at the other doctors for their decisions about who needed surgery or other issues. At times he was upset with me as well.

One bone of contention was over the issue of publicity and the internet. The internet came along full-blown in the mid 90's and I obtained a URL, MindBodyMedicine.com and put up the first website about TMS around 1997. The website's original design included material to educate people about TMS. It included some biographical information about me and a list of other practitioners doing this work. Of course, I listed Dr. Sarno at the top of that list, as a deserved honor as the founder of this work.

Surprisingly, when he saw the website, he was upset. He was angry at me for including him on the site without his permission. This was not an issue of endorsement. In fact, he did not want to be listed at all. He explained to me that in his books, there is no phone number or office address. He preferred patients find him through the telephone book or hospital operator. Of course, when he explained this, I honored his wishes and removed his name, address, and phone number from the website.

In some ways, Dr. Sarno was very old-fashioned. He was trained in the days before doctors were allowed to advertise, before doctors and hospitals promoted their services, and long before the internet. In some ways, his practice developed in the most modern of ways, but he remained passionate about the old ways. Remember, his practice of TMS blossomed after a New York magazine article, grew dramatically with the publication of his first two books, and a few key media appearances (e.g. 20/20). Despite this, he preferred not to be listed on the internet.

I mention these examples because I learned from Dr. Sarno that people are different, and one must understand their preferences clearly. I also learned that a founder, a creator, an innovator can clash with some of those that follow his ideas. These clashes are usually about the core concepts of the diagnosis and treatment but can also be about the ways it is presented. These types of conflicts are very common in the history of medicine, science, and psychology. Think of Freud and Jung, Oppenheimer and Teller, etc. The different branches of a tree whose trunk is a Sarno, a Freud, an Einstein.

LESSON SIXTEEN

There may be challenges with having a powerful, strong-minded mentor

---

So, the relationship had its ups and downs, however I greatly appreciated the TMS referrals that his office was able to provide, so I did my best to keep things calm and smooth. Sometimes this led me to speak to him less often or less deeply than I might otherwise have. But it felt necessary. Eventually, my own referral sources developed, from my website, patient word of mouth, my Workbook, some media appearances, and the like. I remain, as of this writing, the only MD in

California truly focusing on this work. There are still way too few physicians nationally and internationally familiar with and incorporating the principles of TMS. However, the number is growing.

CHAPTER 7

Meeting others, expanding
the Psychology Network

This network started with Don Dubin, MFT. My psy-chotherapy referral network that is. Don's practice began to get very busy with my referrals. He intro-duced me to a couple of therapists that he thought would be interested in the work. I typically had lunch with an interested therapist and discussed TMS. I rec-ommended they read *Healing Back Pain* and we talked some more. They began to receive a few referrals and we talked about the patient's progress on the phone or by email. Gradually they became more adept at the work or it was apparent from patient feedback, etc. that they were not appropriate to do TMS psychotherapy.

There was no formal training program. No train-ing program at all. Just me working with psycho-therapists and helping them become TMS specialists. Intermittently, another therapist would approach me, and the process continued. A couple were my patients at one point, but most just gravitated toward this interesting and meaningful type of work.

Psychotherapists and psychologists are generally supportive of the TMS concept. They learn about emotions and the body in their training, but not TMS specifically. Those trained in pain psychology are often the least attuned to work in the TMS model because their expectations are often too low for success, for cure. Pain psychology training focuses on managing pain. Goals are set at a 10 or 20% reduction in pain. TMS is a different way of looking at the ability of a person to get rid of pain completely, even while they may not solve all their emotional issues.

At this point, I am incredibly pleased at the "cluster" of therapists in the greater LA area that I refer to. Some have added junior associates and trained them in the work. A few had started their careers renting space in my office. This closer collaboration is effective, but they have always eventually moved on to their own office, their own space. The most dramatic example of this is Alan Gordon, LCSW, who after working in social work for a while, began to concentrate on therapy and specifically TMS therapy. In just a couple of years he went from renting space in my office to starting a group, to renting a huge office suite, to building the largest group of TMS related therapists in the world, the Pain Psychology Center. He has really expanded the awareness of this work.

It is not surprising to me that psychotherapists would be more amenable to this kind of work than physicians. The study of psychology includes an emphasis that physical conditions can be caused or worsened by stress. Some programs go further in their study of 'psychosomatics' as it has traditionally been called. But that does not mean that psychologists automatically realize the power of this work. I find that they need to have experienced powerful results with patients, or family members, or themselves to really understand this.

Dr. Sarno's work benefitted from the proximity of Arlene Feinblatt, Ph.D and later Fran Anderson Ph.D and Eric Sherman Psy.D. He referred a considerable number of patients to these therapists and their trainees and to other therapists mostly in the New York area. A question from some patients is, "I thought Dr. Sarno only referred 20% of his patients for therapy, or 15% or 30%? So why are you recommending I see someone?" The implication is that they are somehow worse if I am recommending this intervention. But Dr. Sarno used different estimates of this percentage in different books that he wrote, and my own practice has developed in a psychotherapy rich environment. I try to help people get better and if I believe that can happen more effectively with a referral and the patient is agreeable, so be it.

For a long time, there was little mixing between the East Coast cluster around Dr. Sarno and the West Coast cluster in the Los Angeles area. But over the years, contact increased, including at conferences. In this era, I sometimes have a patient that I feel might do better with a particular New York therapist and the L.A. Therapists have many video visits with clients in other states. Of course, this is done within the constraints of state licensing and other rules of these professions.

I continue to believe that ideally, a physician should diagnose TMS and that a referral to a TMS therapist should then follow, where appropriate. I do understand that the reality in the world is that this sometimes occurs in the opposite fashion. There are also book cures; people who are cured just by reading one of the books on this subject. So getting to healing clearly happens in different ways for different patients and I am totally fine with that.

CHAPTER 8

Ann Arbor and Beyond

OVER THE EARLIEST YEARS OF my TMS practice in Los Angeles, 1995-2005, a few doctors reached out to me to ask about the work. There was at least one chiropractor who took an interest and quite a few calls from physicians (M.D.'s) beginning to formulate their own approaches to TMS treatment. I offered advice and help and usually listed these individuals on my website as well.

Over time, Marc Sopher became well known in New England, Andrea Leonard-Segal in D.C., Howard Schubiner in the Midwest and others. But contact with TMS colleagues was limited and fleeting during this period. I mostly worked in isolation with occasional careful contact with Dr. Sarno.

Then Howard Schubiner and John Stracks planned and organized a conference in Ann Arbor Michigan, not too far from Howard's practice location near Detroit. He asked me to speak at the conference and

I accepted. I even convinced five TMS therapists from LA to travel with me by plane to the conference! The conference weekend was a tremendous experience because I had never been around so many people who "got it". We spoke the same language; we saw medicine in a similar way. It was wonderful interacting with so many people during that weekend.

Dr. Sarno was supposed to attend the conference, but due to distance and the burdens of aging, he elected not to attend. He also became upset at some things he had read about that Dr. Schubiner was incorporating into his TMS work (again, I wrote earlier of an intolerance to differences in approach). So, he needed some calming down, which Howard was moderately successful at doing so. Ultimately, he did speak briefly to the conference via speakerphone. I recall speaking to him and saying how wonderful the conference was. He quipped that we could have held earlier conferences in a closet, and he was pleased the movement was growing!

CHAPTER 9

The SMI Research
Foundation, 2005-2008

I knew and the TMS community knew that we needed more research to support the tremendous clinical work that we were all doing, based on the pioneering work of Dr. Sarno. So, when an affluent patient, whom I helped with TMS pain, asked me how we could make this work more well known, I agreed to lunch at a Beverly Hills area hotel.

Our discussion focused on his interest in recruiting and training more doctors and my interest in pursuing and publishing research in this area. Ultimately, he agreed to fund both projects, and despite a shoestring budget (by research standards), I was able to hire a part time assistant, and set aside a small amount of time each week to work on this Foundation.

This led to several publications that I co-authored with Arthur Smith, Ph.D., Foundation Coordinator, along with research assistants, some of whom are now physicians. It included a significant effort to find physicians, but this proved challenging despite our best efforts (magazine ads, sending free books, etc.). Everyone involved in the research was a co-author (or strongly acknowledged in the articles)—see Lesson Eight (a) above.

The Foundation funding ended around the time of the financial crisis of 2008-09 which affected the ability of the Foundation's financial backer to continue his support. Towards the end, I had finally met the right people to do the functional MRI imaging study that I wished to do, but the timing was not right.

LESSON SEVENTEEN

High Quality medical research is difficult to do, expensive, and requires an infrastructure such as a University or teaching hospital's support. A team is essential.

CHAPTER 10

Dr. Sarno's movie and his passing

TOWARD THE END OF DR. Sarno's life a movie premiered in New York called *All the Rage*. Created by Michael Galinsky, a Sarno patient, it features Michael, Dr. Sarno and his New York psychology colleagues, with cameos by me and other physicians in the national TMS community.

While not a perfect movie, it expanded the ability of prospective and active patients to share this work with spouses, friends, and others. I understand Dr. Sarno was able to attend the premiere and enjoy the experience. He passed away soon thereafter.

The end of the movie featured a wonderful "Thank You Dr. Sarno" book presentation which also occurred at the point at which he lost his office space at the Rusk Institute to upcoming construction and decided in his late 80's to retire from the practice of medicine.

Dr. Sarno became quite ill during the years after his retirement and before his passing. He succumbed

to heart failure in 2017. A New York Times obituary described his remarkable career. I was honored to be mentioned in this piece. Despite his remarkable contributions to NYU and IRM, very little was said or done in terms of noting his career, at the time of his death by that institution. Even a magazine sent out to alumni about back pain that year failed to mention his work or TMS.

When I wrote to an NYU medical school Dean about this, the answer was "many of my patients were helped by his efforts... they sought him out on their own". "I'll see what I can do". I never heard any more from him or about this. Sad, but true.

CHAPTER 11

Telemedicine and Beyond.

The PPDA, etc. 2020-present

THE PANDEMIC HAS BEEN AWFUL in so many ways. But one of the consequences was a temporary expansion of telehealth capabilities, licensing changes, etc. that allowed physicians to do medical consultations on video both in their state and in some cases out of state as well.

For my practice, I was able to reach a lot of patients who were unable or unwilling to travel to Los Angeles for a consultation. While in person medicine is still the best option, telemedicine is a close second for TMS patients who have no local options. On the telehealth platform, one can see one another, look at MRI images that have been sent in advance, share the screen, and other marvels of the modern age.

Unfortunately, after the pandemic emergency was declared over, medical licensing rules have reverted.

Telemedicine is more restricted based upon licensure and malpractice insurance coverage. Medicine seems like the only profession that seems to go backwards at times, at least as pertains to modern technology and its capabilities. Dr. Ira Rashbaum (who took over Dr. Sarno's practice when he retired and continues to be on faculty of the Rusk Institute) and I were recently discussing the role of telemedicine and the challenges of obtaining privileges to do this in multiple states.

During this time, I have also become more involved as an active Board Member of the national non-profit organization called the Psychophysiologic Disorders Association (PPDA). We meet virtually, on Zoom monthly, and have put on two virtual conferences and created other programs for patients and for therapists and doctors. The organization is very focused on increasing the awareness of TMS/PPD and there is such a need for this increased awareness. Dave Clarke MD, now retired from practice, spearheads the effort and is President of the PPDA.

CHAPTER 12

The future of TMS

In some ways, this is the greatest time for TMS. More patients are interested in alternatives to medication and surgery. More scientific data has accumulated about the role of the mind/brain in chronic pain. Patients and doctors are exposed to more mind-body concepts than before, and more articles are published in lay media and medical arenas.

The internet, youtube, websites, podcasts, TV appearances, the TMS wiki; there is lots of free and paid information about TMS available to patients, much of it of high quality (and some not so).

At the same time, as the number of psychotherapists (social workers, marriage and family therapists and psychologists) has expanded with expertise in this area, the number still falls short of the need.

The bigger need is for a vast expansion of physicians understanding TMS and doing this work. But this is a challenge. Physicians practice mostly what they were trained to do in medical school and residency. They are trained to prescribe medications, do injections, and do surgery. Psychiatrists are even mostly focused on medication prescribing. Holistic or functional medicine doctors often over focus on dietary supplements and other external aids.

Residency programs are not training physicians about TMS nor are they producing more biopsychosocially focused physicians. In addition, the reimbursement for private practice physicians, and for hospitals, is far greater for procedures than it is for listening, teaching, and guiding patients to heal in this manner. One might think that the cost savings of this approach would be a powerful incentive in some settings, but I have learned that even in HMO settings like Kaiser Permanente, the constraints of practicing what you were trained to do takes precedence.

LESSON EIGHTEEN

It's a long road to a paradigm shift. A long way to go.

I remain hopeful and I do see evidence of us nearing a tipping point on this, but.... but it sure takes time. It has taken many decades since Dr. Sarno first conceptualized this work and it has taken my entire professional career.

Final Thoughts

On an optimistic note, the PPDA is growing, the training programs for therapists on PRT (a variant of TMS therapy described by Alan Gordon), and other methods of care are exposing more practitioners to this diagnosis and approach and its power to heal.

I remain hopeful that a great idea, a great truth, can't be ignored by the larger conventional medical community forever and I work weekly to educate and expose doctors and medical students to these concepts.

I hope and believe Dr. Sarno would be proud.

I thank him for his teaching and support of my practice, especially in the earlier days. Rest in Peace, my mentor, my colleague, my friend.

We remember his great contributions and honor his 100th birthday in the year this book was written.

References and Partial Bibliography

George L. Engel. Science April 8, 1977. A Need
for a New Medical Model. A Challenge for
Biomedicine. p. 129-136

John E. Sarno: all his books

David Schechter. *Think Away Your Pain.* MindBody
Medicine Publications. 2014.

David Schechter. *The MindBody Workbooks*–Original,
Volume 2, and Teen.

Andrea Leonard-Segal, Eric Sherman, Arlene
Feinblatt, Frances Sommer Anderson. *Breaking out
of Pain.* Atmosphere Press. 2023.

Michael Galinsky. *All the Rage.* Movie released in
2016. Rumur Film Studio.

Appendices: Letters, Photos

Appendix A. A letter from Dr. Sarno referencing a holiday gift.

John E. Sarn

12/22/14

Dear David,

Holiday greetings and
best wishes to you for the
new year.

We shall enjoy the wonderful
salad condiments you so kindly
sent. Marthe's salads are
regular parts of our dinners and
your thoughtful gift will be
regularly used and much
appreciated.

Our family, including the
youngsters, enjoy good health.
We enjoy each others company
and spend as much time as we
can together.

All the best to you

John

A letter from Dr. Sarno   December 22, 2014.
Transcription:

Dear David,
Holiday Greetings and best wishes to you for the
New Year.

We shall enjoy the wonderful salad condiments you so kindly sent. Martha's salads are
regular parts of our dinners and your thoughtful
gift will be regularly used and much appreciated.

Our family, including the youngsters, enjoy
good health. We enjoy each other's company
and spend as much time as we can together.

All the best to you,
John

Appendix B A letter from Dr. Sarno November 19, 2014.

A letter regarding the publication of my book, *Think Away Your Pain.*

11/19/14

Dear David,
I'm happy to have received the copy of your book and I congratulate you. Your support of my work is appreciated.

Warm wishes for a successful publication.

All the best to you and your family for happy holidays.

John

Transcription of above letter:

Dear David,

I'm happy to have received the copy of your book and I congratulate you. Your support of my work is appreciated.

Warm wishes for a successful publication.

All the best to you and your family....

John

Appendix C

Finishing on a bright note. A visit with my family to New York. Circa 2005.

Visiting Dr. Sarno, at his office, behind his desk, with my two young sons (now in their early 20's).

When I see this picture, I think of days gone by and I think of John E. Sarno, 1923-2017. Thanks from your first "medical son". Rest in peace.

MINDBODY MEDICINE PUBLICATIONS

Made in the USA
Las Vegas, NV
02 May 2024

89344858R00046